A Collection of
CHILDREN'S STORIES

Book Savvy International
1626 Clear View Drive, Beverly Hills California 90210, United States

Hotline: (213) 855-4299
https://booksavvyinternational.com/

Ordering Information:
Amount Deals. Special rebates are accessible on the amount bought by corporations, associations, and others. For points of interest, contact the distributor at the address above.

In addition: Each story has its own copyright registered with its author.

Printed in the United States of America.

ISBN-13   Hardback   978-1-961204-44-7
           Paperback   978-1-961204-39-3
           eBook   978-1-961204-38-6

Library of Congress Control Number: 2023908895

A Collection of
CHILDREN'S STORIES

VOLUME 1

WRITTEN BY
ANGELA DELLAFIORA FORD,
WITH CONTRIBUTING AUTHORS

Book Savvy International Inc.
Success is waiting for you...

The authors of this book
would like to give a special acknowledgement
to Dr. Ed May.

CONTENTS

Horatio, the Baby Elephant

Angela Dellafiora Ford

Illustrated
by
Lois Faye Reed

"Horatio, the Baby Elephant" is the first in what will be a series of stories about an elephant who would like to attend children's tea parties but can't because of his size.

This story teaches that everyone is special even though they may be different from others. It also demonstrates how perceived weaknesses can be strengths.

Once upon a time, there was a small town named Littleton.

Near the town of Littleton, there was a small country road where a baby elephant lived with his parents.

The baby elephant's name was Horatio.

Horatio was gray in color and he had big blue eyes. He wore a blue shirt and brown pants.

Every day Horatio would visit the children in the small town of Littleton because he had one wish.

That wish was to be invited to one of the children's tea parties so that he could eat crumpets and drink tea and make friends.

But the children who lived in the small town of Littleton did not want Horatio to attend tea parties because he had one problem.

The problem was that even though Horatio was a baby elephant, he was very, very big.

Horatio could not sit on the chairs because they were too small for him. He could not drink from the teacups because his paws were too big and they would get stuck in them.

This made Horatio very sad, and he cried. It seemed as though his wish would not come true.

One day as Horatio was sitting and crying under a tree near the small town of Littleton, a little girl walked up to him.

The little girl had blonde hair and big blue eyes. She wore a pink dress.

When the little girl saw that Horatio was crying, she became very concerned. The little girl introduced herself as Brenda and then she asked Horatio why he was crying.

Horatio told her that he had one wish and that he was sad because it would not come true.

Brenda then asked him to tell her his wish.

Horatio told her that he wished that he would be invited to a tea party so that he could eat crumpets and drink tea and make friends.

Brenda explained to Horatio that all the children in the small town of Littleton have tea parties and that maybe he could attend one of them.

But then Horatio went on to explain to her that even though he was a baby elephant, he was very, very big.

He told her that he could not sit on the chairs because they were too small for him. He also explained that he could not drink from the teacups because his paws were too big, and they would get stuck in them.

After Brenda heard why Horatio was crying, she wanted to help make his wish come true. She thought for a moment and then told Horatio not to cry and not to be sad.

She told him to meet her under the same tree the next day because she wanted to help make his wish come true.

The next day when they met, Brenda had a brown basket and a big brown barrel that she rolled down the hill.

When Horatio saw Brenda carrying the brown basket and rolling the big brown barrel down the hill, he wondered what was inside them.

When Brenda saw Horatio's curious face, she smiled because she knew that soon he would be a very happy elephant.

In the basket, was a blanket to sit on, a teapot and a teacup so that Brenda could drink her tea. Also, inside the basket was a silver tray filled with delicious crumpets to eat.

Then Brenda told Horatio to look inside the big brown barrel.

When Horatio looked inside the barrel, he could see that it was filled with piping hot tea.

Now Horatio could sit on the blanket and drink his tea from the big brown barrel.

Brenda made Horatio very happy. Now his wish was coming true with her help. Horatio was now able to attend tea parties and eat crumpets and drink tea and he had even made a new friend.

Horatio and Brenda became the best of friends and they continued their parties for a long, long time.

Horatio and Brenda had tea parties on the hills and in the valleys and by the streams.

One day a big storm was approaching the small town of Littleton as Horatio and Brenda were having one of their tea parties.

Brenda and Horatio were having such a good time that they did not notice the storm as it came upon them. As it started to rain and hail, a big gust of wind picked Brenda up and blew her up, up and away.

Soon the children of the small town of Littleton became concerned because they could not find Brenda. They started to cry because she was nowhere to be found. Finally they gave up their search.

Horatio continued to look for Brenda everywhere. He looked for her along the small country road. He looked for her on the hills and in the valleys and by the streams.

Horatio finally found Brenda on the top of a big oak tree. The children of the small town of Littleton were happy when they saw that Horatio had found Brenda in the tree.

When the children saw Brenda on top of the big oak tree, they tried to reach up and get her down. But they could not. They were too little.

The children became very sad and they started to cry because they could not get their friend Brenda out of danger.

When Horatio saw that no one could help Brenda, he thought for a moment. He then told the children not to be sad and not to cry because he could help get Brenda out of danger.

Horatio then walked over to the big oak tree and lifted Brenda out of it with his big trunk.

Now the children from the small town of Littleton were very happy because Horatio helped Brenda safely to the ground. Horatio was a hero.

All the children gathered together and gave Horatio a big outdoor tea party.

There were big, round tables where teapots and teacups and silver trays filled with delicious crumpets.

And of course, there were big brown barrels filled with piping hot tea for Horatio.

Now, once a year, in the small town of Littleton, there is the "Annual Horatio Tea Party" and all the children, and of course Horatio, celebrate this very festive occasion.

Angela Dellafiora Ford

Pork Chop and Polka Dot

Illustrated by Kendis Chase

"Pork Chop and Polka Dot" is a love story of two dogs that are different from each other due to different lifestyles.

This story shows children acceptance of others that could be culturally different from them. This story can also teach children patience.

This story is in what will be a series of stories in which one can meet these two characters' families and friends.

Once upon a time, a very special dog lived in a big city. The dog's name was Pork Chop. He got his name because he loves pork chops. He was a big, black dog with a sturdy build and white-tipped tail. Pork Chop was special because he had a unique sense of smell that enabled him to locate fires from miles away. When Pork Chop smelled a fire, he would blow his big, shiny, silver whistle that he always wore around his neck. When the firemen would hear the whistle, they would quickly jump into their big red fire truck and follow Pork Chop to the fire to put it out.

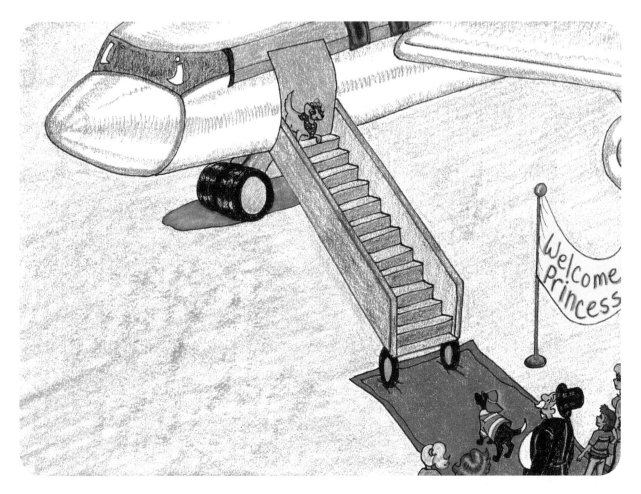

One day, Pork Chop received a telephone call from the Mayor of the city. He told Pork Chop that another special dog was coming to visit the city. This dog was a princess from a far away land. She decided to visit the city to learn more about our culture and society.

When the princess arrived at the airport, the Mayor and the people who lived in the city held up big signs welcoming her. They also rolled out a red carpet and presented her with a bright-colored bouquet of flowers.

Pork Chop was stunned when he first saw the princess. He thought she was absolutely beautiful. Her mane was golden with long, blonde tresses. Her eyelashes were so long and thick that they almost touched her eyebrows. She wore a magnificent crown of family jewels on her head. She also wore a polka-dotted scarf around her neck.

Pork Chop quickly introduced himself. She responded by saying, "I am Princess Polkadotavich." Pork Chop knew that he would have a difficult time pronouncing her name, he asked her if he could call her "Polka Dot?"

Without hesitation, she said, "I don't see why not. Everyone else does." She said she's been called Polka Dot for such a long time that she grew an affinity for the clothing and all accessories with polka dots on them. She told Pork Chop that she was well known throughout the fashion industry for her own line of clothing.

As they were talking, all Pork Chop could think about was how wonderful and beautiful she was. He wondered if she would go out on a date with him. Finally, he mustered up the courage to ask her if she would like to take a walk in the city's park sometime. Without hesitation, she said, "Yes."

But as the days went by, Polka Dot was too busy to spend time with Pork Chop. This was her first visit to the city and she was too busy visiting all the museums and art exhibits. This saddened Pork Chop because he wanted to get to know her better before she returned to her homeland.

One night, as Pork Chop was getting ready for bed, he smelled a fire. Immediately he reached for his whistle on his nightstand. He blew the whistle as loud as he could for the firemen to hear.

When the firemen heard the whistle, they quickly got into the big, red fire truck and followed Pork Chop through the city streets. When they arrived at the fire, Pork Chop realized that it was the "City Hotel" where Polka Dot was staying.

Pork Chop looked up at the tall building and saw Polka Dot standing behind her window crying out for help. He knew she was in great danger because he could see dark smoke surrounding the room all around her.

Pork Chop suddenly remembered the special ladders in the fire truck that could reach the top of tall buildings. Pork Chop yelled to the closest fireman to him, "Drive the fire truck closer to the building so I can save Polka Dot."

Pork Chop was then raised to Polka Dot's room by the special ladder. He quickly opened the window and reached inside for Polka Dot. He held her in his arms as he motioned for the firemen to lower the ladder.

As soon as Polka Dot was safely on the ground, she thanked Pork Chop for his outstanding bravery. Now she knew that he indeed was a special dog. From that time on, they were inseparable.

As the days went by, Pork Chop and Polka Dot began spending time together. They would take long walks in the park, visit the zoo, and go to the movies. It was inevitable that they would fall in love. Now this changed everything. Polka Dot decided not to return to her homeland but to marry Pork Chop and live in the city.

Their wedding day was a joyous occasion. The Mayor and the firemen and the people of the city attended the ceremony. Everyone thought Pork Chop looked so handsome in his black and white tuxedo. They also thought Polka Dot looked radiant in her long, white-lace wedding gown dotted with black pearls.

Pork Chop and Polka Dot were happy to be married because now they could spend as much time with each other as they wanted. The Mayor and the firemen and the people of the city were also happy because now they had two special dogs living in their city. Everyone also knew that it would only be a matter of time before they would have a litter of extra special pups running around.

"The Bell That Would Not Ring"
is a very short and funny story that teaches
us never to underestimate anyone.

THE BELL
THAT WOULD NOT RING

Written by

Bertha T. Dellafiora

Many years ago, there was a bell that sat in the middle of a town square. The people of the town wanted to hear the bell ring, but they did not know how to make it ring. Day after day, the bell sat quiet on the ground in the town square.

One day a little boy decided to ring the bell. He sat down on the bell and tried to ring it, but it would not ring. The little boy started to cry.

A jester strolled into town and saw the little boy crying as he was sitting on top of the bell. The jester asked the little boy why was he crying. The little boy explained that he was crying because he could not get the bell to ring.

The jester told the little boy to get off the bell. He then sent the little boy to Mr. Smith's hardware store to get a ladder and a strong rope. News of the jester had spread through the town and soon a crowd of townspeople had gathered to watch.

The jester went to a big, strong tree in the Town Square. He put the ladder against the tree. He then took one end of the rope and put it into the hole at the top of the bell. Next, he carried the bell up the ladder and tied it to a strong branch on the tree.

The jester then came down the ladder and took the other end of the rope and pulled it up and down. For the first time ever, the towns-people heard the beautiful sound of the bell ringing.

The townspeople laughed and clapped their hands. They all sang this song:

The town bell would not ring,
until the jester came along.
Now the town bell sings this
song:

Ding-dong, ding-dong,
come along and sing this song.
The town bell would not ring,
until the jester made it sing.

The townspeople were so pleased with the jester that they made him Mayor of the town. As Mayor, the jester appointed the little boy to be in charge of ringing the bell.

Now the bell rings everyday at noon and on holidays. The townspeople get just as excited as the very first time that they heard the bell ring.

The Farmer's Horse
and The Farmer
and the Skunk

Written by
Joanie Ranney

These two very short stories are about a farmer
and the love he has for his family and friends. These
stories demonstrate love and kindness.

THE FARMER'S HORSE

Once upon a time, there was a farmer who was feeling down. He asked his wife if he could spend some time alone with the horses. His wife was happy to keep the children with her for awhile and decided to make a trip to the store with them. As they drove away in the van, the children waved happily at their father to say good-bye.

The farmer walked slowly to the barn toward the horse's stall thinking over his problems. It had been a very dry summer and his crops were not producing very much as a result. He thought about all the nice things that he wanted to do for his wife and children but money was scarce.

When he reached the barn, he found one of his horses to be missing. He could not figure out how Snowball had escaped, but he decided he had better go out looking for her. He quickly mounted up his horse Blackie and took off over the rolling hills behind his house.

It was already late afternoon and the farmer galloped faster and farther, calling out her name from time to time. "Snowball...Snowball..."

Suddenly, the farmer stopped. His eye had caught a glimpse of some bushes that were unnaturally broken. He went closer and found horse tracks in the soft ground heading for the creek.

The farmer followed the tracks calling Snowball's name as he went along. He had to dismount Blackie because the ground that was leading down to the creek became quite steep and rocky. The water level was very low due to the lack of rain.

Then the farmer spotted Snowball. He called her name and she lifted her head but did not get up. She had twisted her leg on the rocky ground and was hot and thirsty from being in the sun all afternoon.

The farmer found some wood to make a splint, tying it with his shirt and belt. He gently urged Snowball to stand up and led her the rest of the way to the water so that she could drink.

Snowball was very happy to see the farmer and when she saw Blackie at the top of the hill, she gave out a whinny.

It was a long and tiring trip home and the sun was beginning to set when they finally saw the farmer's house. As the three of them neared the barn, the farmer's wife and children saw them and ran to meet them.

"We were worried about you," said the farmer's wife as she hugged him and as the children hugged the horses.

The warmth and the love of his family around him, along with the happiness of having Snowball safely back home, made the farmer realize that his problems were not what were most important after all.

THE FARMER AND THE SKUNKS

Once upon a time, there was a farmer who was feeling very blue. So he went for a walk through his fields. The smell of the earth as he walked always helped to cheer him up.

As he was walking, he heard a slight rustle in the first row of corn. Because it was evening, it was hard to see, but lo and behold it was what he thought he saw—a whole family of skunks.

The skunks were beautiful—all of them with dark black shiny fur and a perfectly straight white stripe down the middle of their backs. Mom and dad skunk were much bigger than the farmer had imagined a skunk would be.

As the farmer watched the skunks cross his path, all healthy looking with their beautiful fur, he could not help but assume that they were eating his vegetables.

After the skunk family was out of sight, the farmer went to investigate and found that indeed a few of his vegetables were missing.

But why not keep peace and sweetsmelling air, thought the farmer. So the skunk family lived happily ever after.

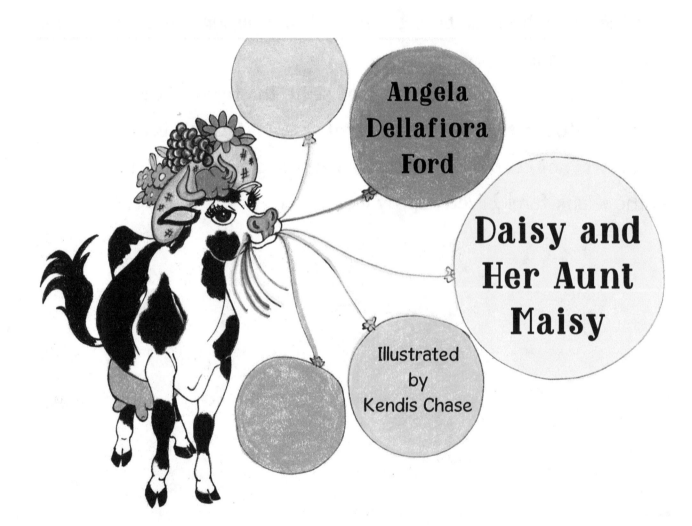

Angela
Dellafiora
Ford

Daisy and
Her Aunt
Maisy

Illustrated
by
Kendis Chase

"**D**aisy and her Aunt Maisy" is a story about a farmer and the care that he takes in making certain that his dairy cows are producers of excellent quality.

The story can teach children that outstanding performance can sometimes obtain high reward. The story also relates how outstanding performance can be used to others in a group to raise their expectations and individual effort.

Once upon a time, there was a farmer who owned a large dairy farm. The farmer's name was John Tucker. Farmer Tucker's cows were well known for producing the best milk in the whole county.

On the dairy farm, there were several large barns in which the cows and their young calves lived. They ate and slept in the barns. The dairy farm also housed special equipment that was used to sterilize and bottle the milk after the cows were milked.

The dairy farm also had a dairy van that Farmer Tucker used to deliver milk to the families, grocery stores, restaurants and cafeterias in nearby towns.

The dairy farm sat on many acres of land. When the cows and their calves went outside, they grazed on the green grass. The grass made the cows healthy and strong. Farmer Tucker thought this was one of the reasons they produced such good milk.

Even though Farmer Tucker took pride in all his cows for providing the best milk in the county, he was especially proud of one cow named Maisy.

Maisy was a beautiful cow. She was large and black and white in color. She had big brown eyes. Maisy was also very strong and healthy.

The reason Maisy was Farmer Tucker's favorite cow was that she produced more and better-tasting milk than any other cow that he owned.

Every year Farmer Tucker would take Maisy to the State Fair. He would enter her into competitions with other cows from the different counties throughout the state.

Maisy would always win the blue ribbon for being the most beautiful cow in the state. She would also win first place for producing the most milk. When the judges tasted the milk from the different cows, they would always vote Maisy's milk number one.

Farmer Tucker loved his award-winning cow. One day, he decided to take Maisy shopping in town so that he could buy her a present to show his appreciation.

Farmer Tucker told Maisy he wanted to buy her a present, and that she could go into the different shops and choose whatever she wanted.

Maisy felt proud of herself and her accomplishments. She was very happy that Farmer Tucker would take time out of his busy schedule to buy her a present. When they arrived in town, Maisy saw many different types of shops. Maisy went into a jewelry store and a women's clothing store. Maisy could not decide what she wanted. She was getting tired when she came upon a hat specialty shop and one hat in the display window caught her eye.

Umm. Maisy thought that this hat was the most beautiful one she had ever seen.

She quickly pointed it out to Farmer Tucker and told him that this is what she wanted.

The hat was big with a wide brim. It was made of light, tan straw. It was filled with bright flowers and berries.

Umm. Maisy thought this hat would be the perfect gift for her. Not only would it look beautiful on her, it would also serve a practical purpose. It would keep the sun out of her eyes while she grazed on the grass on the farm. Pleased that the hat made Maisy happy, he bought it for her and they drove home.

When they returned home and the other cows saw Maisy with her new hat, they were a little envious. Oh, how they wished they could own a hat like hers.

Soon all the cows were standing around Maisy admiring her present. They told her she looked absolutely lovely in her new hat.

Again, Maisy was very happy and proud of herself. Not only could she produce the most and best-tasting milk in the county, she was also a beautiful cow who was wearing a pretty hat. All was well with Maisy's world.

As the days went by, one could always find Maisy grazing on the farm wearing her new hat while the other cows stood around admiring her.

As Maisy and the other cows grazed on the farm, Farmer Tucker continued to be busy with other chores. Not only did he have to attend to the regular duties of the cows, but he also had to take care of their young ones.

Farmer Tucker needed to tend to the calves because they were his investment in his future. He had to make sure that they were fed properly and that they had adequate sleep. He wanted them to grow up to be strong and to be able to produce the best milk in the county.

Farmer Tucker was especially interested in one young calf named Daisy. Daisy was Maisy's niece and in many ways Daisy reminded the farmer of her aunt.

Daisy was black and white and had big brown eyes and she definitely had her aunt's beauty. Daisy was also big and strong for her age.

Even though Farmer Tucker loved his Maisy, he knew that soon she would be too old to produce milk. He was hoping that when that time came, Daisy would be able to replace Maisy as the State Fair.

One morning as Farmer Tucker tended to his chores, he heard Daisy moo. It was a very loud moo. Farmer Tucker now knew that soon Daisy would be fully grown and able to produce milk.

Daisy continued to moo that morning and even though Maisy was absorbed with her hat, she soon noticed the loud moo.

Although Maisy loved going to the State Fair and winning first place, she knew, as did Farmer Tucker, that it was just a matter of time before she would be old and unable to produce milk. Maisy decided that Daisy was now ready to enter the State Fair competitions.

Maisy then walked over to her niece and said, "Well, well, well, how big and strong and beautiful you have grown up to be. You look exactly like me."

Daisy then told her aunt how much she admired her and that she liked her hat.

"This hat is my pride and joy." Maisy said to her niece, "It came from one of the finest stores in town. Farmer John bought it for me because I always win blue ribbons at the State Fair. It comes around once a year, you know." Maisy continued on, "Now that you are full grown I shall take you with me. Now that you are big and strong and beautiful, you can enter the contests. You will not have a problem winning the beauty contests since you look like me. Your milk should be as good as mine since we are from the same stock."

It was spring time and the State Fair was only a few months away. Farmer Tucker and Maisy would have all summer to prepare Daisy for the competition at the fair that opened in early fall.

Farmer Tucker made sure that Daisy was not only grazing and eating the good grass but that she was also getting adequate sleep so that she could produce good milk.

Aunt Maisy taught Daisy how to have good posture and how to walk correctly so that she could perform well in the beauty contest.

Aunt Maisy showed Daisy all the blue ribbons that she had won over the years. Daisy was proud of her. She was hoping that she could win blue ribbons too.

Daisy felt a little nervous. She had worked hard to prepare for the fair. She did not want to disappoint her aunt or Farmer Tucker.

Time passed quickly. It was now early fall and time for the State Fair had arrived. Farmer Tucker and Maisy took Daisy to the fair and entered her into the competitions. Daisy truly was beautiful and healthy and strong. It looked as though their hard work would pay off.

Maisy then noticed that Daisy was looking upset. Maisy reassured Daisy that even if she did not win the blue ribbons at the State Fair, she and Farmer Tucker would still love her.

Maisy then realized now that Daisy was more important to her than ever. She told Daisy that at times her self-interest got in the way of her love for her. Maisy promised that in the future she would make sure that this would not happen again.

Daisy was now uplifted and more determined than ever to do her very best.

Daisy loved the State Fair with all the different types of food and colorful displays. She liked the games and rides. Daisy also enjoyed people coming to the fair to look at her in the competitions.

Daisy did indeed win first place for producing the most and best milk at the State Fair. Of course, Daisy would win the blue ribbons for being the most beautiful cow in the state. Farmer Tucker was so proud of his two award-winning cows. Maisy was so proud of her niece. Daisy was now a happy and proud cow.

On their way home from the day's events, Maisy asked Farmer Tucker to stop in town to buy Daisy a hat just like hers. It was Maisy's way of showing her appreciation for Daisy.

Now Daisy had a hat just like her aunt's. When they returned home, all the cows gathered as Daisy showed them her blue ribbons and new hat. All in all, it was a big day for Daisy. She was tired and she went to bed very early that night.

Because of Farmer Tucker and Maisy's hard work, Daisy had indeed grown up to be exactly like her aunt.

As the days went by, Farmer Tucker thought how abundant and good his life was because of his cows. He wanted to show his appreciation to all of them.

Farmer Tucker quickly drove into town. When he returned home, he had bought all his cows and their calves a present. He told them this was because he appreciated and loved them very much. He also told them he was proud of all of them.

Now, one can find all of Farmer Tucker's cows grazing on the grass wearing hats just like Daisy's and her Aunt Maisy's.

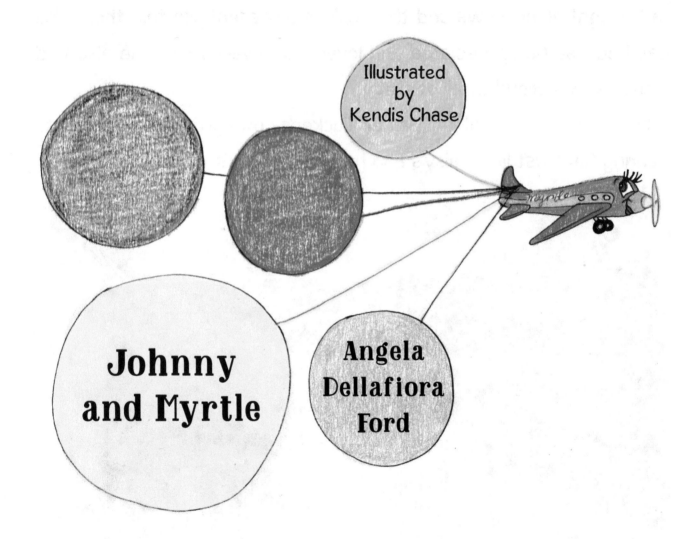

Johnny and Myrtle

Illustrated
by
Kendis Chase

Angela
Dellafiora
Ford

66 "Johnny and Myrtle" is a story about a young boy who meets a very old, rundown airplane named Myrtle and how they help each other's dreams come true.

This story simply states that just because something is old does not necessarily mean that it is not good and cannot be used.

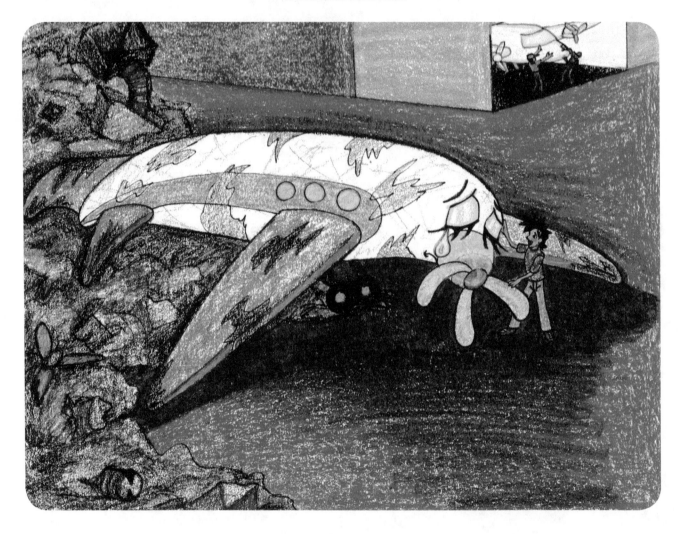

There once was an airplane names Myrtle. Myrtle was a small plane and she was white in color with blue and gray stripes.

Myrtle was an old plane and no one wished to fly her. She needed a new paint job, an oil change for her engine, and her propellers and wings needed mending.

Myrtle was put in the junk pile at the airport. It was only a matter of time before she would be taken apart and would not exist anymore. Newer airplanes were coming into being and they were faster and more efficient than poor, old Myrtle.

Every night when Myrtle went to bed, she would dream that someone would fly her. Myrtle missed going to different lands and visiting places that were fun and exciting to see.

Myrtle knew a young boy named Johnny. Johnny was twelve years old and his father worked as an airplane mechanic at the airport. Sometimes after school Johnny would ride his bicycle to visit his father at work.

Johnny loved the airplanes and he hoped that one day he would be a pilot. Every night when Johnny went to bed, he would dream of going to different lands and visit places that were fun and exciting to see.

One day when Johnny was at the airport watching his father and the other mechanics working on the airplanes, he and Myrtle started to talk. They told each other their dreams. Myrtle told Johnny that if she were not such an old plane that needed repairs, he could fly her.

They would then be able to go to different lands and visit places that were fun and exciting to see. Then their dreams would come true.

Johnny then decided to give Myrtle a new paint job. He would also give her engine an oil change. He would also mend her propellers and wings. He would then be able to fly Myrtle and they could go to different lands and visit places that were fun and exciting to see.

One early Saturday morning, Johnny awakened very early. He quickly rode his bicycle to the airport. He went to the hangars and started to look around for materials to fix Myrtle up and make her fly.

Johnny found red, orange and yellow paint. He found a toolbox with a hammer and a screw driver and nails. He found the oil to lubricate Myrtle's engine. Johnny then took all these materials to the junk pile where Myrtle was and went to work.

After Johnny mended Myrtle's wings and propellers, he gave her engine an oil change. After the oil change, he painted her bright red and orange. After the paint dried, he wrote her name in yellow paint on both sides of her.

Johnny could not believe how beautiful Myrtle looked with her new paint job and with her parts mended. Johnny and Myrtle were both so happy because now Myrtle was as good as new. Johnny would now be able to fly her.

Johnny told Myrtle that he would go home and get some canned food and utensils to put inside his backpack so they would have food to eat if they got hungry on their travels.

He also told Myrtle he would go to bed very early that night. His parents would think he was upstairs sleeping, but he would crawl out his bedroom window and ride his bicycle back to the airport so they could begin their journeys.

First, Johnny and Myrtle decided to visit a faraway place known as "The Big Forest." Johnny started Myrtle's engine and after many hours of flying, they came upon a big forest.

After landing Myrtle in a clearing, Johnny and Myrtle decided to take a look around. The trees were so big and beautiful that it overwhelmed them. The leaves on the trees were bright orange, red, brown and green.

As Johnny and Myrtle were walking around the forest, Myrtle started to point out the different types of trees to Johnny. Myrtle showed Johnny a big oak tree and an elm tree. She also showed Johnny what redwood trees looked like.

Johnny cracked open the nuts from the pecan trees and fed them to the squirrels and the deer in the forest. Johnny also fed some rabbits that were hopping around and fed them some pecans also.

Myrtle decided to go rock hunting and she found all different types and sizes of rocks and stones that she and Johnny could bring home with them. She found bluish-green stones that were very pretty. Myrtle told Johnny that he always admired turquoise stones.

Johnny and Myrtle came upon a stream and they decided to take a swim. As they were enjoying themselves in the water, they noticed that the fish were swimming alongside them. This made both Johnny and Myrtle laugh. Johnny and Myrtle also saw ducks wading in the water.

Johnny and Myrtle were quite pleased with their visit to "The Big Forest." They said good-bye to their new friends who were the squirrels, the deer and the rabbits. The ducks also wished them well on their way. Johnny and Myrtle were now ready for their next rendezvous.

Their next visit was to "The Animal Kingdom." In "The Animal Kingdom," Johnny and Myrtle saw animals that they never saw before. They saw giraffes, hippopotamuses and kangaroos. They also saw a black-and-white-striped animal called a zebra.

Johnny and Myrtle saw monkeys climbing trees and vines. They also saw many different types of exotic birds and enjoyed a wonderful conversation with a parrot.

As Johnny and Myrtle were making friends with the animals, a kangaroo picked Johnny up and placed him inside his pouch. The kangaroo then gave Johnny a ride in his pouch by jumping up and down.

It was getting near dawn and Johnny and Myrtle were getting tired and hungry.

They built a fire in the jungle and they ate the canned food that was in Johnny's backpack. They then made beds with large bamboo sticks so they could sleep for the night.

As they were almost falling asleep, they heard big noises. They got up to see what it was and they saw a white lion and a big, black bear playing tag with each other.

When the two animals saw Johnny, they started to chase him because they wanted to play tag with him. Johnny became very frightened of these two animals and started to run away.

As Johnny was yelling for help, Myrtle quickly started up her engine and propellers. She then flew and picked Johnny up by his pants. Myrtle saved Johnny from the two animals chasing him. Then they went elsewhere to rest for the night.

When morning came, Johnny and Myrtle said good-bye to all their friends that lived in "The Animal Kingdom" including the white lion and the big, black bear.

Johnny and Myrtle then took off for "The Enchanted Land."

When Johnny and Myrtle came to "The Enchanted Land," they met a man riding a magic carpet. Johnny went for a ride with the man on the magic carpet while Myrtle followed closely behind. The magic carpet took Johnny and Myrtle to "The Enchanted Castle."

Inside "The Enchanted Castle," Johnny became friends with the princess who lived there. Her name was Lila. She was a very pretty princess who lived with her parents who were the king and queen of "The Enchanted Land."

The princess and Johnny played with the magicians and jugglers of the castle. Johnny had such fun with the magicians because they would find coins behind his ears. Johnny also had fun watching the jugglers toss bright colored balls around all at one time.

After playing with the magicians and jugglers, the princess gave Johnny a magic wand. When Johnny waved the wand, the toys started to move. The wooden rocking horse started to rock back and forth. The drummer doll started to play his drums and the dancing doll started to dance. Johnny had such fun watching the dolls march up and down the room.

The princess then took Johnny out to "The Enchanted Garden" and every time Johnny planted a seed, a flower would pop up and grow. Johnny grew many different types of beautiful flowers with these magical seeds. He grew daffodils, gladioli, pansies and lilies.

Finally, Johnny and Myrtle decided to depart for home. They thanked the princess for her fine hospitality and waved good-bye to the king and queen and the magicians and the jugglers. The man on the magic carpet flew beside them for a while to set them on their way.

As Johnny and Myrtle were descending towards the airport, people started looking up and pointing at them.

Johnny's father and the men he worked with also looked up and saw them.

When they touched the ground, all the people stood around Myrtle admiring her bright colors. The people thought Myrtle was a fine looking plane.

Johnny's father was quite surprised to see Johnny flying this small plane. After everyone heard about their experiences, Johnny's father had an idea.

It was now decided by Johnny's father and the other mechanics that Myrtle was to be kept in good shape by Johnny.

The reason Myrtle was to be kept in good, running condition was so that she could fly small groups of people to different lands and visit places that are fun and exciting to see.

Now Johnny keeps Myrtle in good shape. He cleans her and keeps her engine oiled and greased so she will never break down again.

Myrtle is now a happy plane. She will not be disassembled and taken apart and she will continue to exist. She doesn't even live in the junk pile anymore.

She now stays in one of the hangars when she is not flying. She is also making many people happy by flying them to different places.

Johnny is a very happy boy because sometimes on the weekends or during school vacations, he will fly Myrtle back to the places they visited to see all their new friends again.

THE AUTHORS & LLUSTRATORS

Angela Dellafiora Ford

Angela Dellafiora Ford was born and raised in western Pennsylvania. She has a Bachelor's Degree in Political Science from Indiana University of Pennsylvania. She has worked for the Federal Bureau of Investigation (FBI), and the Department of Defense in Washington, D.C. Angela has studied acting at the Maryland Academy of Dramatic Arts and Theatre in Silver Spring, Maryland. Over the years, she has performed on stage and in films. Angela lives near the Chesapeake Bay in Maryland with her husband, Alan, and two cats, Ricky and George.

Jaonie DeKorne Ranney

Joanie DeKorne Ranney was born and raised in Grand Rapids, Michigan. She has a Bachelor's Degree in Psychology from Calvin College in Grand Rapids. Ms. Ranney also attended the Sheffield School of Interior Design. Ms. Ranney is a restaurant owner in Virginia. Joanie likes to play golf and walk and enjoy the outdoors. She has a son with her late husband, Mike, named Joseph. Joanie currently lives in Alexandria, Virginia.

Bertha Tedeshi Dellafiora

Bertha Tedeschi Dellafiora was born and raised in western Pennsylvania. She was a wife and mother to four children and a grandmother to three. She worked for the state of Pennsylvania and also for a tax accountant. She owned her own business—National Beer Sales, for twenty-five years.

Lois Faye Reed

Lois Faye Reed was born and raised in Washington, D.C. She graduated from the University of Maryland with a degree in Interior Design. Ms. Reed was the Coordinator of Interior Design at the Woodward and Lothrup Department Store in Washington, D.C., for thirteen years. She is in the "Who's Who of the World," "Who's Who in America," and "Who's Who of American Women." Ms. Reed is the past President of the American Institute of Interior Designs.

Kendis Chase

Kendis Chase was born in Mystic, Connecticut, and raised in California, where she currently resides. Ms. Chase is an award-winning artist who has excelled in film, television, and onstage.

9 781961 204393